Hello! My name is Luna. I wa[...] what my life is like as a "lefty."

Hi

One day I was coloring with my purple crayon. Purple is my favorite color. I was drawing a beautiful purple flower when suddenly my Mom said to Dad, "Look, Luna is using her left hand!"

The excitement in the house made it clear that I had something special! From that point on, I was known as a "lefty."

I then found out my Grandma used her left hand to write and color, too! Grandma was very excited to hear my big left-handed news! She said this gave us a special connection! She also told me that only 10% of the people in the world use their left hand to write! That means most people use their right hand to write.

They called it my dominant hand. That means it's the hand I use the most. I couldn't wait to tell my friends I was a lefty!

Shortly after that, my Mom signed me up to play T-ball. I thought it was going to be so much fun! It was, but I couldn't share my glove with my friends or use their glove to catch the ball.

That's because I put the glove in my right hand so I could throw the ball with my left hand.

My friends did the opposite. I also stood on the opposite side of home plate, compared to my right-handed friends.

I may do things a little differently than others, but boy do I just love to play T-ball!

In school, it was time for math. My teacher asked me to write a math problem on the dry erase board.

I was so excited to be picked! Sadly, my hand drug over the top of the numbers and smeared part of what I just wrote! I couldn't believe it and the class was shocked! Thank goodness my new friend Randi was there.

She handed me a tissue to wipe off my hand. She's a lefty, too! That is how she knew I was going to need that tissue to clean my hand. She is such a great friend.

At dinnertime I heard my mom yell, "It's time to eat!" My little brother Ollie and I would race to our kitchen table. I usually won, but only because I was older and faster.

We always laughed when we got there and sat right next to each other. Eating dinner next to Ollie was funny because we were always bumping elbows.

I used my left hand to eat and he used his right. Well, it was funny until one day we bumped elbows a little too hard. I spilled my milk! Mom said we needed to switch places and that helped.

Later that day I was getting hungry for dessert. My Mom said I could help her make brownies.

My favorite! The recipe needed a half cup of oil. Mom said I could pour it all by myself! I held the measuring cup with my left hand.

I carefully starting pouring the oil in the cup. To my surprise, I had to stop! I didn't know how much I was pouring because the words were on the other side! I turned the cup around to see the writing.

Problem solved! The brownies were delicious!

As time went on, I realized there were several things I experienced that I did exactly like my right-handed friends.

However, there were other things that just didn't feel okay. My Mom told me to call Grandma. She would understand and have some helpful advice.

So I did.

"Have you ever needed to talk to somebody about something that was bothering you?"

The next day Grandma picked me up and took me out to her favorite coffee house.

I was happy because they have the best hot chocolate! This is when we sat down at a table and she started to explain to me all the things that would feel the same as my right-handed friends, and the things that would feel different.

Here are a few things Grandma started to list as we waited for the waitress to bring us our hot chocolate.

- I can only use half of my spiral notebook paper because the wire spiral is in my way - feels weird
- Riding a bike - feels the same
- Zipping up my coat - feels weird
- Doing a cartwheel – feels the same
- Building a snowman - feels the same
- Holding scissors – feels weird
- Shaking someone's hand means I have to use my right-hand – feels weird
- Swimming with friends at the beach - feels the same

Our hot chocolate arrived just after Grandma was done giving me those examples.

We both ordered hot chocolate that had a smiley face on the top made with cream.

Unfortunately, when I grabbed the mug with my left hand, the smiley face turned upside down. It looked like a sad face!

My Grandma saw how disappointed I was and said, "Watch this." She grabbed her spoon, dipped it into her hot chocolate and spun that frown upside down.

Then she said to me, "Now that's the way to live your best life!"

Here are some more things that lefties feel differently than righties:

Opening a book
Using a computer mouse
Starting a car
Car cup holders
Tying your shoes
Swiping a credit card
Can openers
Playing the guitar
Winding up a garden hose
Tape measures are upside down
Mugs have the picture on the opposite side

Can you list any more examples?

1.

2.

3.

Made in United States
North Haven, CT
09 May 2022

19053973R00015